D0046176

Mind-Bending Challenging Optical Puzzles

LAGOON
BOOKS

Series Editor: Heather Dickson
Research: Gaby Wirminghaus, Rosie Atkins
Page layout and cover design: Linley Clode

Published by:
LAGOON BOOKS
PO BOX 311, KT2 5QW, UK

ISBN 1899712690
© LAGOON BOOKS, 1999
Lagoon Books is a trade mark of
Lagoon Trading Company Limited.
All rights reserved.

Printed in Singapore.

MIND-BENDING
CHALLENGING
OPTICAL PUZZLES

INTRODUCTION:

This book contains a colourful mix of puzzling pictures and pictorial puzzles. Some are classic optical illusions, where colours, perspective and depth combine to play havoc on your brain; others are mind-bending logic puzzles and brainteasers which have a vital visual element.

So, if you are ready for the ultimate visual challenge; turn over, train your eye and test your IQ!

Can you stare at this design without your eyes constantly shifting out of focus?

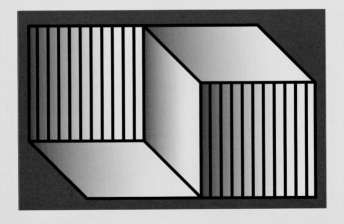

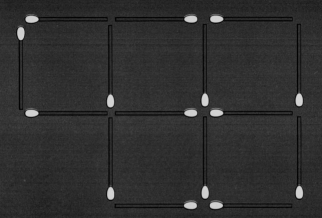

Remove three matches to leave only three squares.

Which are the perfect squares?

Are you sure?

Can you crack the code and find out what the note says?

L44F L4
21FG3S4 FP4
GTP22M Q5F4
5F L3SK3QPF

How many paperclips can you count?

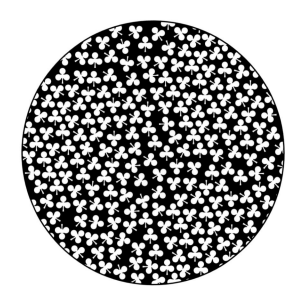

Can you find the four-leafed clover?

If you pulled on both ends of the rope, would the rope knot?

A regular pyramid has four faces that are equilateral triangles and each one is painted either red, blue, green or yellow. The pyramid is rotated and these four different bird's-eye views are made by looking down on each of its four corners?

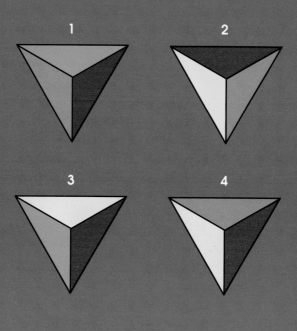

Which one of the views is incorrect?

Stare at the centre of the two gates.
Then, very slowly, bring the page towards
your face and see what happens to the gates.

Turning over two coins at a time, can you make each coin appear tails up in exactly three moves?

Which one of the cubes shown below cannot be made from this flat one?

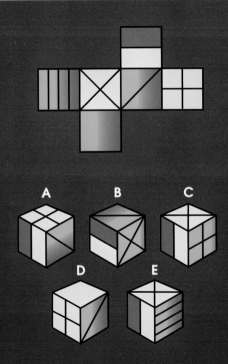

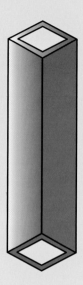

An impossible bar, or is it?
(Turn the book around and look at
the bar from every angle.)

A B C

D E F

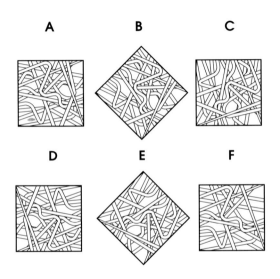

Which pattern is the odd one out?

Can this map be coloured with just three different colours, red, yellow and blue, so that no two countries touching each other are the same colour?

Pick sixteen cards from a pack, the four kings, four queens, four aces, and four jacks. Now arrange them in a 4x4 square so that there is no card of the same suit next to each other along each row, column, or main diagonal.

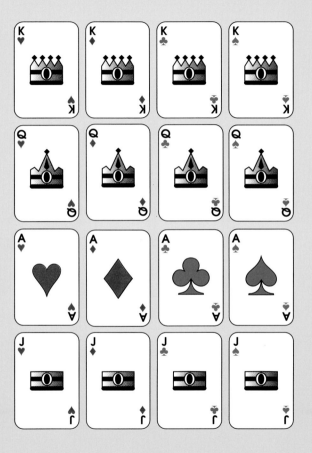

What comes next in the sequence?

1	3	7
15	31	63
127	255	?

Can you find the figure hidden in the picture above?

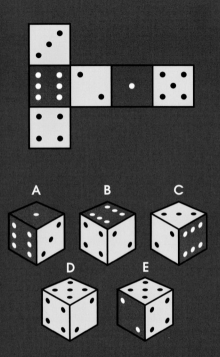

When the dice above is folded, it will look like one of the five dice. Which one?

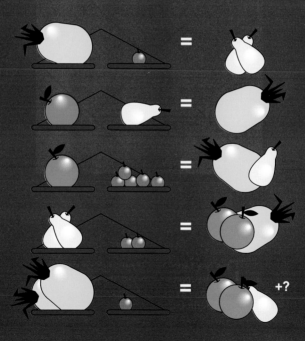

The first four sets of scales balance. What fruit needs to be added to the final set of scales to achieve an exact equilibrium?

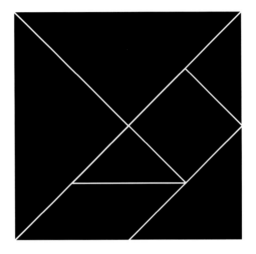

This is a tangram. Thousands of shapes can be made from just these seven. Cut the pieces of the tangram out of card and experiment.

These four shapes are examples of what can be created. How are they made?

Do you see a flower, or a row of concentric circles?

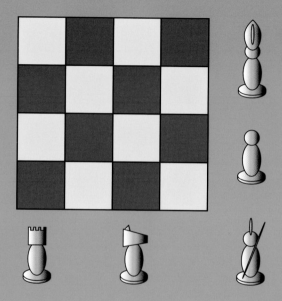

You have four pawns, three knights, three horses, three castles and three bishops. Place them on the grid so no alike pieces are next to each other (vertically, horizontally, or diagonally).

Move the coin and just three matches and make the fish swim in the other direction.

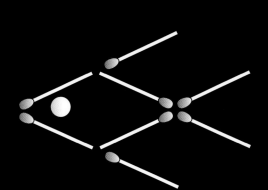

How many rectangles on a chessboard?

Arrange these five cards so that each card touches the other four cards.

Which of the two men is larger?

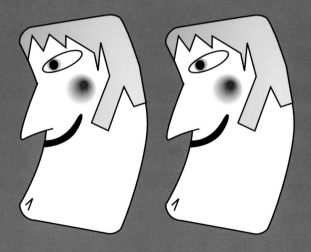

Which of these two envelopes can you draw without lifting pen from paper, and without going over any line a second time?

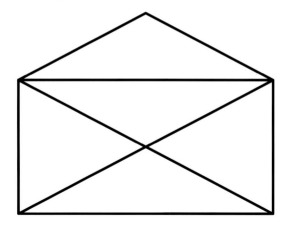

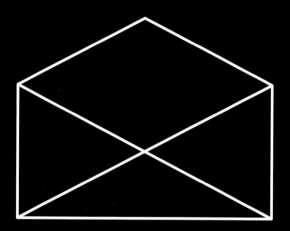

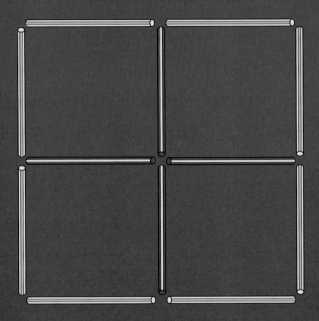

Arrange these twelve straws to make six equally sized segments.

Are looking down onto the pyramid
or are you looking into the pyramid?

How many triangles can you count in this picture?

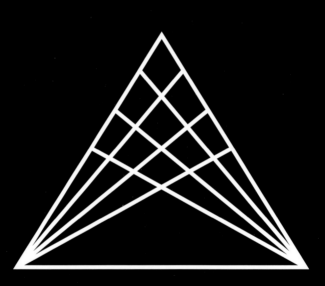

These matchstick Roman numerals show that six plus two equals five. Reposition just one match to make the sum correct.

A   B   C

D   E   F

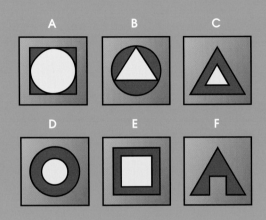

Choose the tile from above that will complete the pattern opposite.

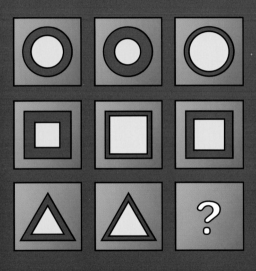

Cut the triangle to form a square.

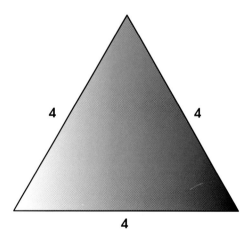

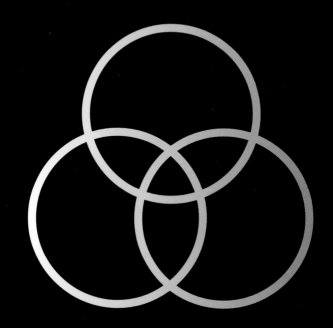

Can you draw the design above without lifting pen from paper or retracing your steps?

Which of these pieces will complete the jigsaw opposite?

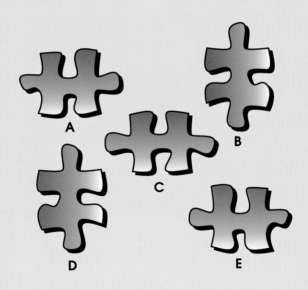

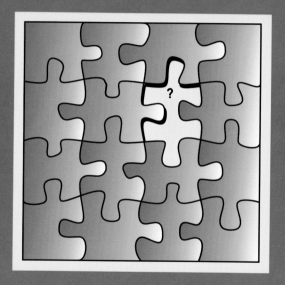

Can you decipher the following cryptic message?

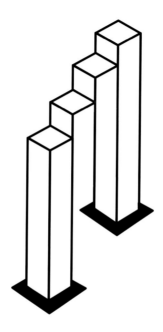

Һow many bars are there?

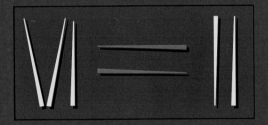

How can you make this equation correct by moving just one toothpick?

Can you draw the arrow and target below without taking pen from paper or retracing steps?

If these views show a bird's-eye view and a head-on view of an object, what is the side-view like?

BIRD'S-EYE

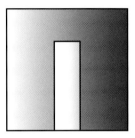

HEAD-ON

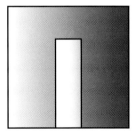

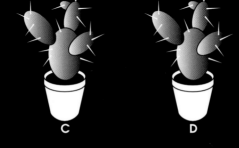

C

D

Which is the odd one out?

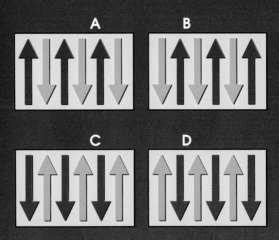

Choose the tile from above that will complete the sequence opposite?

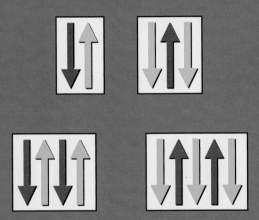

Divide the shape into four parts of equal shape and size.

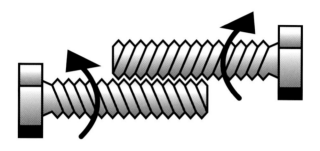

The bolt on the right above would be screwing into a nut, the bolt on the left would be unscrewing. If these two bolts are touching, do these movements bring them closer together or further apart?

Beginning with the letter 'E', at the top of the triangle, and reading down, always passing from a letter to an adjoining letter, how many ways is it possible to read 'Equilateral'?

W hat is the ratio of the areas of these two equilateral triangles?

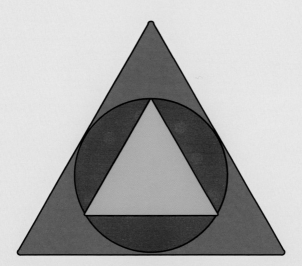

Place these fourteen dots along the side of a square in such a way that there are an equal number of dots along each side.

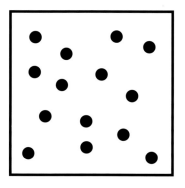

One barrel has oranges (O), one has lemons (L) and one has a mix of both oranges and lemons (M). All three have been incorrectly labelled. How can you tell which is which if you are only allowed to pick one piece of fruit from just one barrel?

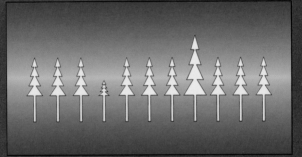

Which tree are you looking at?

Are your eyes drawn to the three cubes at the outside of this design or the cube in the middle?

Which of these two webs are identical?

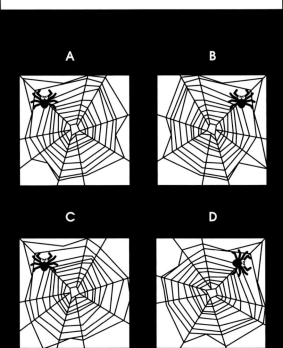

A

B

C

D

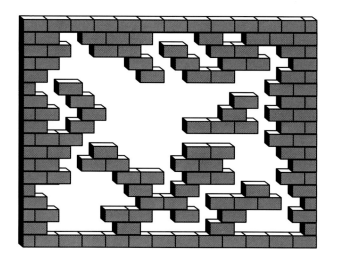

How many bricks are missing from the wall?

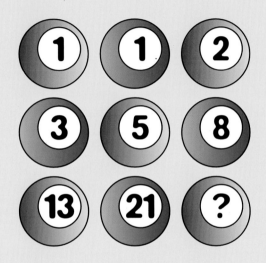

What comes next in this sequence?

You have three empty cups and 10 peanuts. Place all the peanuts into the cups so that there are an odd number of peanuts in each cup.

Choose the tile from below that will complete the pattern opposite.

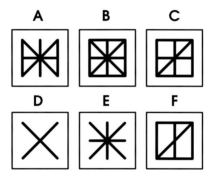

A

B

C

D

E

F

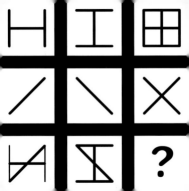

The circumference of each log above is two feet. If the logs were rolled forward until they had made one whole revolution, how far forward would the block of stone have moved?

Divide this cake between four children so that each child gets a piece with two smarties which is exactly the same size and exactly the same shape as the pieces given to the other three children.

Which one is the odd one out and why?

A

B

C

D

E

F

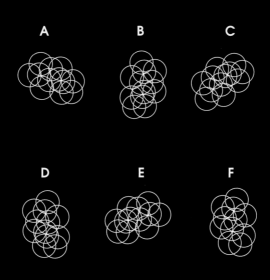

Can you find the five-pointed star?

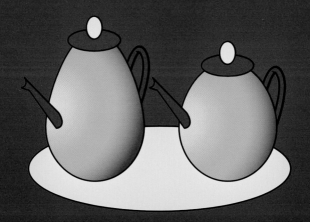

Which tea pot will hold the most tea?

Which is bigger, the line between A and B or B and C?

Should the 'Z' go inside or outside the box?

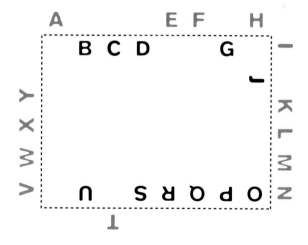

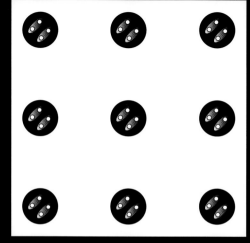

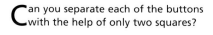

Can you separate each of the buttons with the help of only two squares?

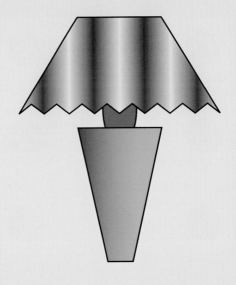

Is the top of the lamp shade longer then the top of the lamp base? If you can't decide, get out a ruler and check!

Can you cut the sphinx into four pieces of exactly the same shape and size?

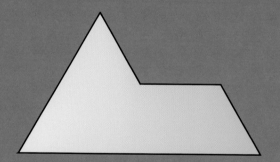

Which dot marks the centre of the circle?

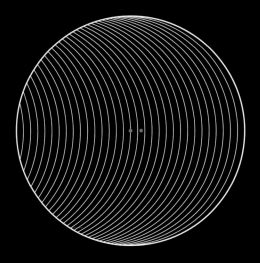

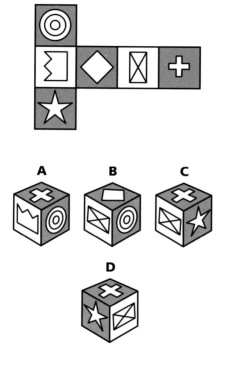

Which is the odd dice?

CARBON DIOXIDE

Take a piece of paper with the words 'CARBON DIOXIDE' on it and hold it up at right-angles to a mirror. The word 'CARBON' is reversed, what happens to the word 'DIOXIDE'?

It looks as if a piece of cake is missing, but is it really?

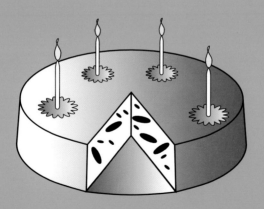

What is in black?

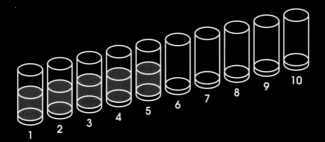

You have 10 glasses in a row and the first five contain liquid, the next five are empty. Can you alternate full and empty glasses by moving just two glasses?

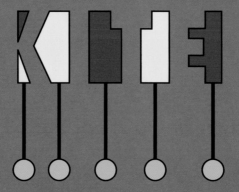

Can you read the word above?

How many rectangles can you count?

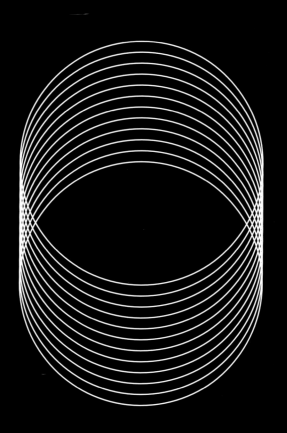

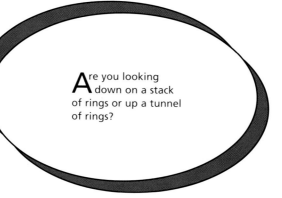

Are you looking down on a stack of rings or up a tunnel of rings?

solutions

Page 7
Take one match from
the middle top row and
the two matches which
form the bottom right
hand corner.

Page 10
Meet me outside the school gate
at midnight.
Code: the consonants are written
using the corresponding letter
of the reversed alphabet and the
vowels are A = 5, E = 4, I = 3,
O = 2 and U = 1.

Page 11
31.

Page 12

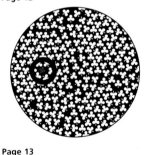

Page 13
No.

Page 14
View 2 is incorrect. The views in
2 and 4 both have green as the
base, therefore 1 and 3 must

be correct. From view 3,
looking at the top-right hand
corner with green as the base,
the correct colours are red,
blue, yellow, which is the same
as view 4, which means that view
2 is incorrect.

Page 17
Start by having the coins: head,
head, tail. Then turn over
1 & 3, 1 & 2, then 1 & 3.

Page 18
C.

Page 20
F.

Page 21
No it cannot.

Page 22
AH KS QC JD
QD JC AS KH
JS QH KD AC
KC AD JH QS

Page 24
511. The numbers are one less
than the powers of 2 ie
$2 - 1 = 1$, $2^2 - 1 = 3$, $2^3 - 1 = 7$ etc.

Page 26
B.

Page 27
A pear and a cherry (pineapple =
16, cherry = 4, pear = 10,
apple = 6).

Page 31

C to E to D to B to A to E to B to C to D.

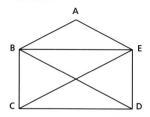

Page 32

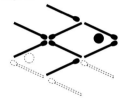

The second one is impossible.

Page 38

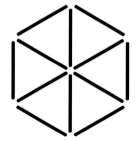

Page 33
1296.

Page 34

Page 40
64.

Page 41
Move the vertical match from the '+' sign and place it in front of the 'V' to make six minus two equals four.

Page 36
The first one – you can go

solutions

Page 42

C.

Page 44

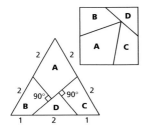

Page 45

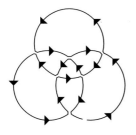

Page 46

C.

Page 48

Well done. The code:

Page 50

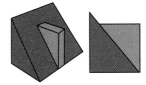

Page 51

This is one solution.

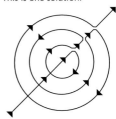

Page 52

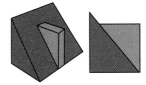

solutions

Page 53
A.

Page 54
C.

Page 56

Page 57
They do not move.

Page 58
1024 ways.

Page 59
1:4. Rotate
the internal
triangle
as shown:

Page 60

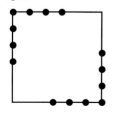

Page 61
Take a piece of fruit from the
barrel marked 'M'. As this is
wrongly labelled it cannot contain
both oranges and lemons. If, for
example, it contains 'oranges' you
know that 'L', which cannot
contain lemons, must therefore
contain the mixture of oranges and
lemons, 'O' must contain lemons.

Page 64
A and D.

Page 65
105.

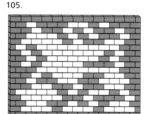

Page 66
34. Each term is the sum of the
two previous terms.
Eg 1 + 1 = 2, 1 + 2 = 3,
2 + 3 = 5 etc.

Page 67
Place seven peanuts into
one cup, one peanut into
the second cup and the
remaining two peanuts
into the third cup, which
you should then place

inside the second cup, so
you have an odd number of
peanuts in each cup.

Page 68
B.

Page 70
Four feet. As each log is rolled
forward, its contact point with
the stone goes backward
along the stone. One complete
revolution will end up with
the log two feet further
back than the stone.
The log is also in contact
with the ground, and one
complete revolution will
take it two feet forward
along the ground. Therefore
the stone will move four feet
forward.

Page 71

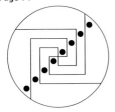

Page 72
F. There are only eleven circles, all
the rest have twelve.

Page 73

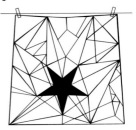

Page 74
The pot can be filled only
to the level of the spout,
so they will both hold the same
amount.

Page 75
The line between B and C.

Page 76
It should go outside the
box because it has straight
line letters.

Page 77

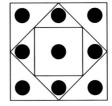

Page 79

Page 82
The word 'DIOXIDE' is reversed too, but its symmetry enables you to read it.

Page 85
Pour the liquid in glass 2 into glass 7 and the liquid in glass 4 into glass 9.

Page 81
D.

Page 87
18.

LAGOON
BOOKS